pocket cornwall

The Geology and Landscape of Cornwall and the Isles of Scilly

Simon Camm

Alison Hodge

First published in 2011 by Alison Hodge, 2 Clarence Place, Penzance, Cornwall TR18 2QA, www.alison-hodge.co.uk, info@alison-hodge.co.uk

ISBN-13 978-0-906720-83-7

British Library Cataloguing-in-Publication Data
A catalogue record for this book is available from the British Library.

Designed and originated by BDP – Book Development & Production, Penzance, Cornwall

Printed in China

Title page: Green saponite or soapstone veins, Kennack Sands, the Lizard

Acknowledgements

I would like to thank Dr Robin Shail for making helpful suggestions on the manuscript, and Mr Bruce Grant for the image of cassiterite in quartz from Cligga Head. The diagram of exposed granites and concealed batholith on page 15, based upon Bott et al, S.W. England British Regional Geology Series 1975 by Edmunds et al, and the geological sketch map of Cornwall on page 30 are reproduced by permission of the British Geological Survey. © NERC. All rights reserved. IPR/127-47CY.

Contents

Introduction

Castellated granite cliffs, looking towards the dark metamorphosed country rocks at Cape Cornwall

Cornwall's spectacular scenery is the result of its long geological history – a journey of some 500 million years. In spite of its small size, the county has a variety of rock types ranging from sedimentary mud and sandstones to igneous intrusive and extrusive ones of granite and those of volcanic origin. Some of the rock types are rare and were formed on the deep ocean floor at mid-ocean ridges. The sedimentary and volcanic rocks have been subjected to earth (tectonic) movements, and have been deformed into folds and subsequently, in some cases, 'baked' by the igneous rocks and hence metamorphosed.

Granite tor, Kenidjack, St Just (above). Greenstone promontory, Gurnard's Head (below)

Cornwall, with the exception of the Isles of Scilly, was not covered by an ice sheet during an ice age; it was, however, subjected to very cold conditions which produced erosion and the formation of rocky, earthy deposits infilling valleys, and wind-blown silts and clays.

Erosion has resulted in a variety of coastal and inland scenery. The hard granite can be seen both in white castellated cliffs and inland in spectacular granite outcrops called tors. The volcanic rocks, especially when 'baked' by the granite are hard, dark green rocks.

The Lizard: Plateau of serpentinite, Goonhilly Downs (above); serpentinite rock and cliffs, Kennack Sands (left)

They are very resistant to erosion by the sea, so occasionally form headlands. These were exploited by prehistoric man for cliff castles. The softer rocks, such as serpentinite, are without any real relief inland, and the dark, soft cliffs are subject to much coastal erosion. Much further away from the granite intrusions, the soft sedimentary rocks are easily eroded, with the rock strata clearly exposed on the beaches between high and low

Coastal scenery of Carboniferous strata, near Bude

water. Deep river valleys have been cut into the landscape, and some flooded by the sea.

The underlying geology can sometimes be detected by the vegetation. On the high moors of granite, as well as lower-lying ground underlain by serpentine, this is usually poor heathland. The softer sedimentary and volcanic rocks sometimes produce rich, fertile soils used for both arable and dairy farming, and are often wooded. Old buildings have utilized this natural rock resource, and are quite different in character as you progress throughout the county. Prehistoric man used the resistant rock, mainly granite, for burial tombs and stone circles. Mining throughout the county, evident from the abandoned engine houses, is testament to the riches of mainly copper and tin recovered by this activity. Quarrying for dimension stone, road stone and slate, as well the recovery of china clay, is still in progress today.

About this Book

Clockwise from above left: Cobbles and boulders of granite, and occasional exotic rocks, tombolo between St Agnes and Gugh, Isles of Scilly; pebbles on Marazion Beach; serpentine and other pebbles, Kennack Sands, the Lizard

Cornwall is my county, and during my formative years, walking along the cliffs and investigating old mining sites, I developed a deep fascination for its geology. My later specialization in the geology of ore deposits led to my becoming a geologist, and in due course Chief Geologist at one of Europe's premier tin mines, and subsequently a mineral exploration manager and consultant. This gave me more of an insight, as then I was seeing the geology not only at the surface but also from the 'inside', in underground mines and drill core. When walking, I am still fascinated by the aesthetic of the rock formations of both

*Clockwise from above left: Greenstone wall,
St Ives; granite cobbles, St Ives; old Cornish hedge
of granite, Morvah, west Cornwall*

cliff and hill. Local geology can be seen in the
pebbles and cobbles on the beach, while
enjoying the amenities and sunshine. Walking
in towns and villages, or even countryside,
there is an indication of the geology underfoot, in buildings or hedging stone when local
rock has been used for construction.

I hope that this book will impart some of
my fascination for the subject of geology. The
county, being a peninsula, has a very long
coastline, much of it accessible on foot. It is
the coastal sections that exhibit some of the

most spectacular rock exposures, illustrating
Cornwall's geological past. I have tried to
choose some of the best examples of this,
but I will never be able to show all as the
book would be far too big! Some are easy to
observe and are self-explanatory; for those
that are not, I have annotated the photo-

Sandstone and rhyolite wall, Kingsand, south-east Cornwall (left). Slate hedge, near Padstow (right)

graphs. I have given a more detailed account of the geology of Cornwall in the next chapter, which is a little more technical. I hope you will excuse this, as I feel it will increase understanding of the geological history, and put it into some kind of perspective for the non-geologist. Also included is a gallery of rocks types which may be encountered in Cornwall, and a glossary of terms which may be useful for the observer.

Most of the sites are on beaches, cliff tops or moorland, accessible to the public; some are on private land or in active quarries. I must stress that many are SSSIs (Sites of Special Scientific Interest), and others have citations as they are Regionally Important Geological and Geomorphological Sites (RIGS) for geoconservation. These can be accessed online – the SSSIs at http://www.sssi.naturalengland.org.uk/Special/sssi/index.cfm, and the Cornwall RIGS group at http://www.cornwallwildlifetrust.org.uk/geology/geology.

It is important that you take only pictures and leave the rock outcrops and the pebbles on the beach untouched for others and future generations to enjoy.

Note: Cliffs and beaches, due to tides and slippery rocks, plus mine workings, are dangerous. Sites are described for your information only. Some areas are on private property, and many are protected sites in order to preserve the geology for future generations; often hammering is not permitted.

Geology

Cornwall's spectacular scenery is the result of its long geological history, which started approximately 500 million years ago (Ma). Some of the oldest rocks of the county have travelled from well below the Equator to their present position in the northern latitudes. The geology records not only the northwards drift but deep sea sedimentation, volcanism, mountain-building, igneous intrusion, metamorphism, mineralization, and erosion. The climate has varied from wet and humid to desert-like, and is now temperate, after a very cold spell during the Quaternary Ice Age – the last glacial period which ended only 10,000 years ago. Younger Permian and Mesozoic rocks, such as red sandstones and chalk seen to the east in Devon and Dorset, are not seen in Cornwall, but are present offshore to the south.

The main story of Cornwall's geological past starts in the Devonian Period, just over 400 Ma, when a northern landmass was being eroded and the sediments deposited in deep marine basins to the south. These sediments generally consisted of mudstones and sand-

Carboniferous strata of mudstones and sandstones showing folds, near Bude

stones and, rarely, limestones. In the deeper parts, the sediments were deposited from submarine flows known as turbidity currents, which resulted in fine and coarser sediments known as turbidites. Submarine volcanic

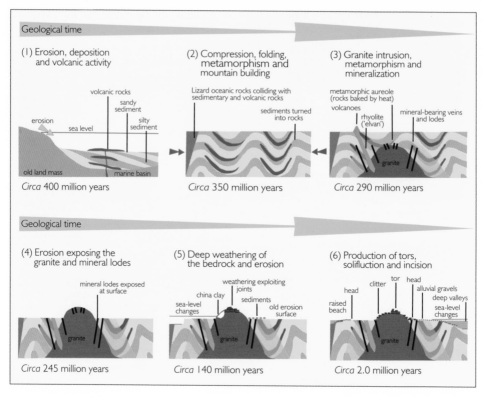

Geological time →

(1) Erosion, deposition and volcanic activity

volcanic rocks
sandy sediment
silty sediment
erosion
sea level
old land mass
marine basin

Circa 400 million years

(2) Compression, folding, metamorphism and mountain building

Lizard oceanic rocks colliding with sedimentary and volcanic rocks
sediments turned into rocks

Circa 350 million years

(3) Granite intrusion, metamorphism and mineralization

metamorphic aureole (rocks baked by heat)
volcanoes
rhyolite ('elvan')
mineral-bearing veins and lodes
granite

Circa 290 million years

Geological time →

(4) Erosion exposing the granite and mineral lodes

mineral lodes exposed at surface
granite

Circa 245 million years

(5) Deep weathering of the bedrock and erosion

weathering exploiting joints
china clay
sea-level changes
sediments
old erosion surface
granite

Circa 140 million years

(6) Production of tors, solifluction and incision

clitter
tor
head
head
raised beach
alluvial gravels
deep valleys
sea-level changes
granite

Circa 2.0 million years

Geological timeline for Cornwall

activity produced basalt lavas forming 'pillows', and sheet-like bodies (sills) intruded the soft seafloor sediments. Volcanic ash deposits are occasionally present, forming sediments known as tuffs. The deeper parts, or feeder system for the mafic rocks such as basalt

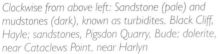

Clockwise from above left: Sandstone (pale) and mudstones (dark), known as turbidites, Black Cliff, Hayle; sandstones, Pigsdon Quarry, Bude; dolerite, near Cataclews Point, near Harlyn

remained more crystalline, forming a dolerite or, deeper still, a gabbro. Later, a collision between continents forced up a piece of the deep ocean floor of dark-coloured ultramafic igneous rocks which now form the Lizard complex. Compression folded the marine sediment of mud and sand into rocks as part of a mountain belt. All these sediments and volcanic rocks have been altered to some degree and are known as metasediments or metabasites – in Cornwall these are known colloquially as 'killas' and 'greenstone'. Due

Clockwise from above left: Peridotite, Kennack Sands, the Lizard; greenstone (pillow lavas), Gurnard's Head, west Cornwall; folding in sediments, Millook Haven, north Cornwall

to plate collision some 300 Ma, in the Late Carboniferous Period, a mountain-building episode named the Variscan Orogeny affected Cornwall, although the process started in the Middle Devonian Period about 380 Ma. During the development of the mountains, these rocks were buried to slightly deeper

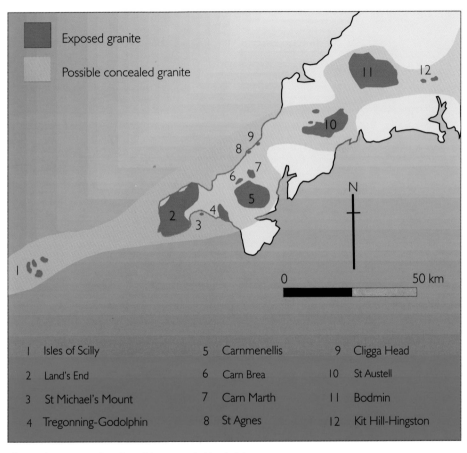

1	Isles of Scilly	5	Carnmenellis	9	Cligga Head
2	Land's End	6	Carn Brea	10	St Austell
3	St Michael's Mount	7	Carn Marth	11	Bodmin
4	Tregonning-Godolphin	8	St Agnes	12	Kit Hill-Hingston

Exposed granites and outline of the concealed batholith

Dark-coloured mafic metabasite (greenstone) and white felsic granite boulders, Porthmeor Cove, west Cornwall (left). Coarse-grained and fine-grained granite sheets, Nanjizal, west Cornwall (right)

levels within the crust and were deformed and modestly heated – a process known as regional metamorphism.

During the Early Permian Period, starting some 295–270 Ma, an igneous intrusion of granite invaded the country rock of sediments and volcanics. The rocks within the lower parts of the mountain chain be-

gan to heat up and melt, and were intruded into the heart of the mountain chain of the Variscan Orogeny. Only small topographic highs, known as plutons, are exposed at surface, as perhaps some 2–3 km have been eroded away. They are all connected to the underlying granite batholith or backbone to the county, which stretches from the Isles

  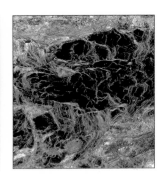

Left to right: Quartz, feldspar, biotite mica

of Scilly into Devon at Dartmoor. Granite is formed from the minerals feldspar, quartz and mica, and is felsic rock having a high silica content. The intrusion exploited weaknesses such as cleavages and fractures in the country rocks. The granite incursion came in a series of pulses, often forming sheets of different texture (grain-size). Castellated granite cliffs and tors are the result of almost vertical joints aligned because of stress, and almost horizontal expansion joints due to the offloading of the weight of rock above resulting from erosion. In the later part of this major intrusive activity, a finer-grained quartz and feldspar rock known as a rhyolite, and locally as elvan, was intruded in thin, nearly vertical, sheets. These were probably the feeders

reaching the surface as volcanoes, and at one locality the lava from such a volcano is visible on the foreshore in south-east Cornwall.

Heat from the granite intrusion metamorphosed the surrounding country rocks of mudstones and volcanics. Very near the contact with the granite, the metamorphism of the country rocks converted the basalts and sediments into a very hard mafic rock, a metabasite or hornfels (very fine-grained, often banded, hard rock), and when highly altered into skarns containing garnet and other high-temperature minerals. The mudstones were also converted into hornfels, or further away into spotted slates containing metamorphic minerals of cordierite and andalusite. This metamorphic aureole

'Baked' sedimentary rock known as hornfels, Botallack, west Cornwall (left). Lead lode formed in a fault with breccia, Port Quin, north Cornwall (right)

extends up to 3 km away from the contact with the granite, the rocks getting progressively less altered further out.

As the granite intruded, there was a build-up of fluids at the highest point in the 'roof' of this igneous rock, containing reactive elements of boron and fluorine. These had the effect of altering some of the minerals in the granite to produce new ones, and altering the country rocks nearby. Occasionally, the fluid pressure would overcome the weight of the rocks above, and would suddenly explode upwards to the surface, producing highly fractured rocks known as a hydrothermal breccia. The granite contained radioactive minerals in the matrix. In decaying, the radio-

Lode structure with red haematite and black tourmaline in granite, Holman's Test Mine, Troon, near Camborne (left). Cliff mine workings for tin ore, St Just, west Cornwall (right)

active minerals gave out heat, and the granite also contained water, making it 'wet'. This hot-wet granite started producing convection cells of hot mineral- and metal-bearing waters with metals leached out of the granite and country rocks. If this hydrothermal water reached the surface it would be known as a geyser. These hot, metal-bearing waters migrated along fractures or faults and precipitated metalliferous minerals due to changes in pressure, temperature or the chemistry of the surrounding host rock, or by mixing with cooler groundwaters. This granite-related hydrothermal occurred 290–260 Ma. Later tectonic activity, some 200 Ma, continued this process. Near-vertical structures

North Cliffs platform, looking towards St Agnes Beacon (above). Old copper mine, Porthtowan, north Cornish coast (left)

containing metalliferous minerals are known as lodes, and these have been exploited by mining for many elements, especially tin and copper for which the county is famous, and also tungsten, arsenic, zinc, lead, uranium, silver, antimony, iron, cobalt, nickel, bismuth, uranium and gold.

Later, as a land mass, Cornwall was subjected to erosion after uplift, and the cover rocks over the granite – perhaps some 2–3 km thick – were eroded. It was then subjected to deep weathering which produced china-clay deposits by the breakdown of feldspars in the

Clitter and tor, Twelve Mens Moor, Bodmin Moor

granite. Later still, high sea-level incursions probably produced sediments which have been eroded, but the planated land surfaces, or plateaus, are still visible as a series of platforms from inland on the granite highlands to others lower down on the coast. The granite hills, so prominent in the landscape, may well have been islands at that time. However, only some very small remnants of sediments of mainly sands and clays of this period have been discovered on the lower platforms at around 120 m AOD (above Ordnance Datum) and below, and none at all on the higher ones.

During the Quaternary Period, from 2 Ma, there were radical changes in the climate known as the Quaternary Ice Age, which produced ice ages in cold spells and interglacials during warmer periods. Although Cornish mainland was not covered by ice, it did impinge on the north coast at one time, and also reached the Isles of Scilly, leaving

Frost cracking of granite, St Mary's, Isles of Scilly (left). Wind-blown silty-clay, known as loess, Lowland Point, the Lizard (right)

glacial outwash gravels known as glacial till. The mainland, however, was subjected to what is called periglacial conditions in the cold phases, when it had a tundra-like environment with permafrost and little vegetation. Rock was broken by ice expansion – a process of freeze-thaw exploiting the joints in the rock – and, in the case of the granite, produced clitter slopes of broken rock debris, and exposed the underlying rock to form tors. During summer melts, clay and broken rock under the influence of gravity 'flowed' downhill to infill valleys, forming the material we now call head. Wind-blown, silty-

Periglacial head and raised beach, St Loy, west Cornwall

clay formed loess deposits around the coast. Icebergs deposited erratics – exotic rocks from far away – on the wave-cut platforms around the coast. In interglacials, when the ice cap melted, sea levels were higher than they are today, forming what are now raised beaches which can be seen around the coast.

At the end of the last ice age, some 10,000 years ago, when sea levels were about

Raised beach on a wave-cut platform overlain by periglacial head, Maen Dower near Nanquidno, west Cornwall

can be seen during storms, when shingle and sand are removed between high and low water to expose submerged forests. Cornish folk memory mentions the lost land of Lyonesse, which would have stemmed from a rapid rise in sea levels during the Mesolithic and Neolithic periods of prehistory. The Isles of Scilly, once a large island, became partially submerged and formed a number of small islands – an archipelago. Deep valleys were eroded during periods of lower sea levels, and with a rising sea level these became submerged and tidal up to many kilometres inland. They are known as rias, and are most pronounced on the south coast. Valley systems were infilled with gravels during summer melts, forming alluvial deposits, some of which were mined for cassiterite (tin ore) up to the twentieth century in placer deposits; in some cases these lay many metres beneath the estuarine muds and are below sea level. Storm beaches advanced inland as the sea level rose, with windblown sand now forming the extensive dunes around the coast.

120 m lower than today, the vast bays such as Mount's Bay and St Austell Bay were land. At one time, before the rise in sea level after the last ice age, it might have been possible to walk to the Isles of Scilly, France and Ireland. Remnants of this old land under the sea

Facing page: Ria, Fal Estuary near King Harry Ferry (top); sand dunes, Hayle Towans, Hayle, west Cornwall (bottom)

Gallery of Rock Types

The gallery below may act as a field guide to the variety of rock types found in Cornwall. Due to the variation in grain size, and hence texture, it is by no means exhaustive, and rocks when weathered can sometimes be difficult to identify. Some of the rocks shown here have been used for local buildings, decorative work, roadstone, hedge-building, etc, and polyphant – an exotic type of greenstone rock – is still used for sculpting and carving.

Granite (coarse-grained)   *Granite (medium-grained)*   *Granite (fine-grained)*

Lithium granite   *China stone*   *Kaolinised granite*

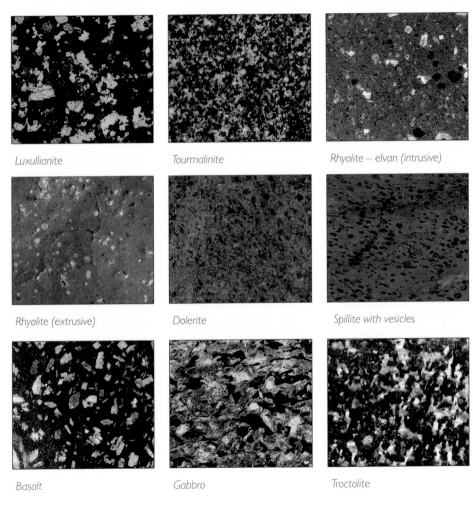

Luxullianite

Tourmalinite

Rhyolite – elvan (intrusive)

Rhyolite (extrusive)

Dolerite

Spillite with vesicles

Basalt

Gabbro

Troctolite

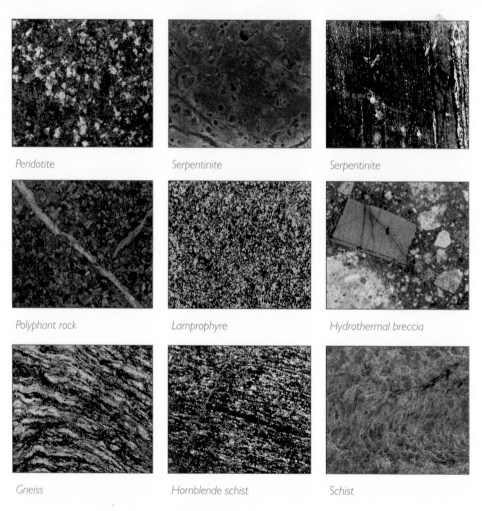

Peridotite

Serpentinite

Serpentinite

Polyphant rock

Lamprophyre

Hydrothermal breccia

Gneiss

Hornblende schist

Schist

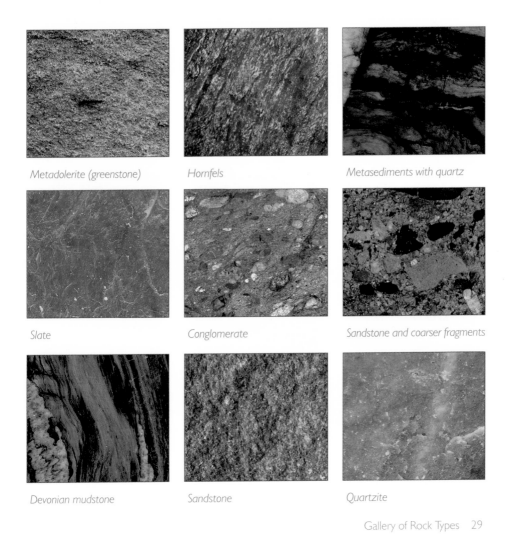

Metadolerite (greenstone)

Hornfels

Metasediments with quartz

Slate

Conglomerate

Sandstone and coarser fragments

Devonian mudstone

Sandstone

Quartzite

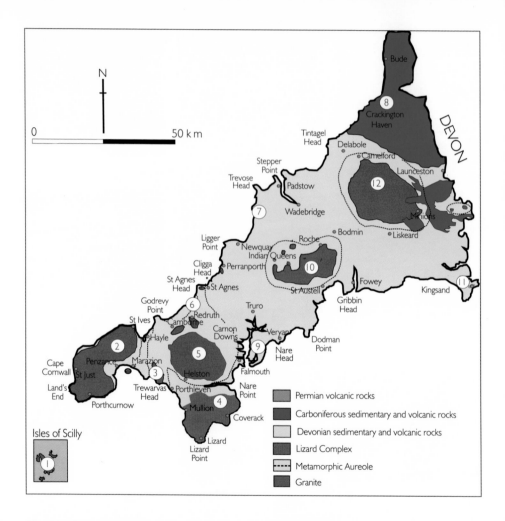

Permian volcanic rocks

Carboniferous sedimentary and volcanic rocks

Devonian sedimentary and volcanic rocks

Lizard Complex

- - - Metamorphic Aureole

Granite

Selected Geological Exposures

Because of the great variety of exposure due to the narrow peninsula and great length of coast, 12 areas have been selected to demonstrate the key features of Cornwall's geology, as most of the sites are accessible or visible. These are shown on the map opposite:

1. Isles of Scilly
2. Land's End: Porth Chapel to Hayle
3. South Coast: Marazion to Porthleven
4. The Lizard: Polurrian to Mên-aver Beach
5. Carnmenellis: Camborne to Helston
6. North Coast 1: Godrevy to Perranporth
7. North Coast 2: Newquay to Trebetherick
8. North Coast 3: Delabole to Bude
9. Falmouth: Carnon Downs to Nare Head
10. St Austell: Indian Queens to Fowey
11. Kingsand
12. Bodmin Moor: Camelford to Minions

1 Isles of Scilly

Coarse- and fine-grained granite contact, Carn Morval Point, St Mary's, Isles of Scilly

Facing page: Sketch map of simplified geology of Cornwall and locations of geological sites

Lying some 48 km to the south-west of Land's End, the Isles of Scilly form an archipelago of about 200 low-lying granite islands. These are connected at depth to the main granite batholith, some 290 million years old, which forms the 'backbone' to Cornwall. Only granite, a crystalline igneous rock, is exposed as the cover rocks have been completely removed by erosion. The granite comprises several separate intrusions, which can sometimes be observed by the different textures in the rock. Exposed now are granite tors on many of the islands where the softer parts have weathered away by exploiting the jointing in the granite, leaving only the more resistant material. On the north side of the island of **St Martin's** are sediments of sands and gravels containing 'exotic' rocks derived from glacial till. This washed out from an ice sheet or glacier which almost touched the Isles of Scilly in the Quaternary some 21,000 years ago. The tongue of ice had flowed down the Irish Sea to the northern part of the Isles, scouring out rocks from what is now the seafloor. During warmer periods between ice ages – interglacials – sea levels

View looking west to Tresco Island from St Martin's, Isles of Scilly

Bread and Cheese Cove, St Martin's, Isles of Scilly (above). Flint and exotic rocks from glacial till in the cove (left)

were higher, producing raised beaches up to 8 m above current sea level. In periods of extreme cold during an ice age in the glacial period, tundra-like conditions and permafrost with freeze-thaw broke up the granite rock. The sea level at this time was up to 120 m lower than the present day. During the period of permafrost, in the summer

Isles of Scilly: Remnant tor, Gunther's Island (top). Porthloo Beach, St Mary's, with cliff of periglacial head on the far side (above)

Isles of Scilly: Raised beach, cobbles in vertical position due to freeze thaw action, near Kallimay Rock, St Agnes (left). Periglacial head overlain with brown loess, Porthloo, St Mary's (right)

surface melting occurred, and the thawed, weathered granite debris flowed downhill under the influence of gravity – a process known as solifluction – forming a deposit known as head. This can be seen infilling valley-like depressions, or forming aprons, now exposed around the coast of angular granite rocks in a matrix of brown, sandy-gravel. Wind-blown silt and clay, known as loess, some 21,000–30,000 years old, occurs on the islands and is exposed in the cliffs as an orange-brown deposit over-lying the head deposits. The islands are slowly becoming submerged as sea levels continue to rise, as they have since the end of the last ice age some 10,000 years ago. The Isles of

View from tombolo between Gugh and St Agnes, Isles of Scilly

Scilly would have been much larger in pre-history, forming one large granite island, as is evidenced by drowned prehistoric settlements which can sometimes be seen between the islands. Bars, or tombolos, of sand, cobbles and boulders – as at **The Bar** on **St Agnes** – exposed at low tide now connect several of the separated islands.

Porth Chapel beach

2 Land's End: Porth Chapel to Hayle

The Land's End peninsula is dominated by the granite, intruded some 295 Ma. The associated mineralization features can be seen in coves and cliff exposures. Country rocks of mudstones and volcanic rocks are also exposed on part of the north-facing coast. However, more recent geology is revealed in the form of clay and sand deposits some 2 million years old, and raised beaches and overlying head from the last ice age which ceased some 10,000 years ago.

Porth Chapel cove has exposures showing that the intrusion of igneous rock of granite resulted in a multiple event, as differences in the texture of rock are clearly visible at certain locations. Subsequent earth movements producing earthquakes at the surface are visible in the form of faults, one of which shows that movement produced a striated,

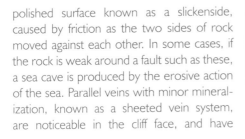

Clockwise from above left: Fault with polished surface known as a slickenside; cave excavation exploiting a weakness in the granite; sheeted veins of quartz and tourmaline in granite

polished surface known as a slickenside, caused by friction as the two sides of rock moved against each other. In some cases, if the rock is weak around a fault such as these, a sea cave is produced by the erosive action of the sea. Parallel veins with minor mineralization, known as a sheeted vein system, are noticeable in the cliff face, and have

Sennen Cove (top). Xenoliths or enclaves of country rock in granite (above left), and large feldspar crystals known as megacrysts (above right), both at Sennen Cove

Porth Nanvan beach showing granite headland, St Just

exploited fractures in the rock. In other areas of Cornwall, when these are cassiterite- (tin ore) bearing, they have been mined for their tin content. In one site, mineralization in the form of green copper staining indicates the presence of copper minerals in the fractures. The cove, for such a small area, has many observable features related to the granite intrusion.

At **Sennen Cove**, the granite lies next to the country rock of slates and volcanic rocks on a wave-cut platform next to the sea. The granite here contains remains of the coun-try rocks as xenoliths, or enclaves. These have been partially absorbed by the very hot liquid magma, and now look like isolated 'dark currants in a white cake'. As the granite intruded, forcing its way into the country rock, fragments were dislodged into the magma. Due to the heat, these started to melt and so became incorporated into the melt. As they are slightly heavier than the granite, they sank, and eventually were com-pletely absorbed, leaving little or no trace. Many are now rounded, often with diffuse edges. Those enclaves which are more

rounded may represent inclusions, or 'blobs' of other magma derived from depth. In the same area are parts of the granite with large feldspar crystals, which indicate a slow cooling under the 'cap' of country rock.

Porth Nanven cove, at the end of the beautiful Cot Valley, has one of the finest examples of climate change of the geological past. Here a storm beach of well-rounded granite boulders forms the lower half of the cliff, covered by angular granite fragments in brown, sandy clay up to the top of the cliff. The raised beach indicates a time when sea levels were appreciably higher than today. This occurred most probably during a warm period between ice ages – an interglacial. We are currently in an interglacial period. Sea levels dropped as an ice sheet grew and expanded to cover part of Britain, with tongues extending down to the Isles of Scilly. Cornwall then had a tundra-like environment with permafrost. During summer melts, the rocks, broken by frost action, and the soil, crept downhill under the influence of gravity to infill the valleys and coves. This material – periglacial head – covered the earlier beach deposits. Later coastal erosion in our more temperate climate has exposed this complete section.

Porth Nanvan: The cliff (top); raised beach overlain by periglacial head (above)

Cape Cornwall with Priest's Cove (above). Folding in metasedimentary rocks now metamorphosed, Priest's Cove (right)

Cape Cornwall is an interesting site, showing more examples of the intrusion of the granite, mineralization, and examples of country rock in **Priest's Cove** at the foot of the Cape. The Cape itself is composed of dark metamorphosed Devonian mudstones and volcanic rocks, in contrast to the pale white granite. Walking down to the foreshore, intense folding that took place before the intrusion of the granite is evident in the country

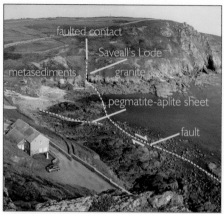

Priest's Cove, Cape Cornwall: Pegmatite and aplite outcrop (above); hydrothermal alteration of the granite has coloured it red (right)

rock. A mineralized fault, **Saveall's Lode**, is exposed in the cliff, with a gated mine tunnel known as an adit. This lode structure has exploited the faulted contact between the granite on one side and metasediment rocks on the other side. Occasionally, this lode looking like rusty iron, which is the iron mineral limonite, is visible extending out on the beach. Cutting across the cove is a sheet of granite, varying from coarse crystalline pegmatite to fine crystalline aplite. These sheets were injected along pre-existing fractures; the grain size variations are related to the rate of magma cooling and, in this case,

Facing page, clockwise from top left: The geology of Priest's Cove; Saveall's Lode; quartz breccia cemented by limonite; Saveall's Lode, showing faulted contact between metasedimentary rocks and the granite

View of the coastal strip showing Botallack Mine and calciner

are influenced by the presence or absence of volatiles (mostly water). On the same side as the lode outcrop is an area in the granite which is highly coloured. This is where fractures in the rock have been exploited as pathways for hot (hydrothermal), mineral-bearing waters which have altered the rock by decomposing the feldspars and colouring them red due to iron in the solution.

St Just to Pendeen is a famous orefield where intensive mining for copper and tin has taken place in a narrow coastal strip. A slender sliver of country rock faces the sea, with the granite a little way inland. The coun-

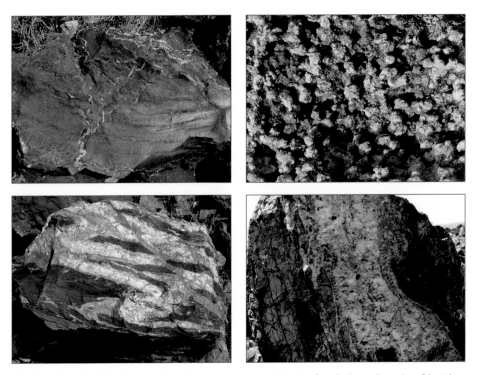

Clockwise from top left: Metamorphosed basalt known as metabasite, Botallack; cordierite hornfels with the harder cordierite mineral more resistant to weathering, Botallack; quartz-feldspar vein, Levant, near Pendeen; folding of quartz in metasedimentary rock, Botallack

try rock contact with the underlying granite inclines gently seaward. These country rocks of mudstones and volcanic rocks have been metamorphosed and hardened into hornfels by the granite intrusion. New metamorphic minerals such as biotite and cordierite have

Clockwise from top left: Secondary copper and uranium minerals, Botallack; Crowns engine houses, Botallack; Grylls Bunny tin floors, Botallack; cassiterite (tin ore) in lode material, Geevor Mine

grown in the mudstones. Fluids expelled from the granite have contributed to the local development of garnet- and magnetite-bearing rocks known as skarns, from the volcanic rocks. The area is mineralogically rich, containing elements of copper, tin, uranium, silver, cobalt, tungsten, zinc, arsenic and trace gold to name but a few.

Pendeen: Levant Mine, engine houses (top). Geevor Mine Museum (above)

Porthmeor Cove: Looking north (above); granite outcrop with batholith roof on the east side of the cove (left)

Near **Botallack** is an unusual occurrence of tin-bearing ore found in flat-lying zones known as floors. Here tin-rich areas have been formed in chemically reactive rocks, now skarns. These have been exploited in an ancient 'tin work' known as **Grylls Bunny**. The steeply inclined mineral-bearing fracture systems known as lodes strike out to sea from

Porthmeor Cove: Granite veins cutting metasedimentary rocks and faulting the aplite vein (left); granite, with pegmatite and aplite, metasedimentary rock contact (right)

the granite country rock contact, and certain mines exploited copper and tin for some 1.5 km out under the seabed, the most famous being Botallack and Levant.

The last working mine on this coast, **Geevor Mine**, closed near the end of the last century and is now a museum. This mine was almost exclusively in granite, but in later years it was connected to **Levant Mine**, in country rock of both sedimentary and volcanic rocks. Samples of the underlying geology can be seen on the numerous mine-waste rock tips in the area.

Porthmeor Cove on the north coast, not far from the spectacular greenstone headland of Gurnard's Head, is a fine example of a small granite intrusion into the country rocks of Devonian mudstones and volcanic rocks,

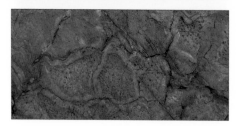

Overlooking Porthmeor Beach, St Ives from Clodgy Point (above). Pillow lavas, Clodgy Point (left). Pillow lavas showing columnar outline (lower left)

now highly metamorphosed, on the east side of the cove. The granite has exploited weaknesses in the country rocks as it intruded into fractures in them, causing blocks to fall into the magma – a process known as stoping, a form of natural mining. Not only is the small granite boss exposed, with pegmatites and aplite veins, but also granitic veins with tourmaline. This is all visible from the west side of the cove.

Clodgy Point, on the western side of Porthmeor Beach at St Ives, has superb exposures of volcanic basaltic rock which erupted under the Devonian seafloor some 370 Ma. Here the 'pillows' of lava are clearly

St Erth Pits (above). St Erth sands (right)

exposed on the point, and with careful examination even polygonal cooling cracks in the lava can be seen. As these are close to the granite contact, they have all been contact-metamorphosed into a very hard, dark rock known locally as a greenstone.

St Erth Pits near Hayle is most unusual and rare in that it contains a remnant of relatively recent geology in the form of clays and sands known as the St Erth Beds. Some 2 Ma, when sea levels were higher, sand dunes were overwhelmed by the sea, and consequently overlain by a marine clay containing fossils. The deposits are about 35–50 m above current sea level. In the early part of the twentieth century, the sands were used for moulding purposes in the nearby iron foundries at Hayle. The pits are now a nature reserve, and partially overgrown, but where animals have been excavating, examples of the sand can still be seen.

sheeted greisen veins with cassiterite and wolframite

granite

metasediments

St Michael's Mount showing granite and meta-sediment contact (top). The causeway (above)

3 South Coast: Marazion to Porthleven

This stretch of coastline includes the scenic island of **St Michael's Mount** with its outcrop of granite-associated mineralization, and the beach at Praa Sands with a rhyolite dyke and very recent geology of peat and clays. Included is the roof-pendant of country rocks in the Tregonning-Godolphin granite at Rinsey Cove, and the extension and contact

Rocks on St Michael's Mount, clockwise from top left: Sheeted greisen-bordered quartz veins, containing cassiterite, wolframite, topaz and other minerals; mineralized vein section with black wolframite in white quartz; sulphide vein of a tin sulphide in granite; greisen veins in metasediments

of this granite in sheets at Tremearne Cliff. At Porthleven there is an erratic from the Quaternary Ice Age, and Devonian volcanic rocks in contact with mudstones.

St Michael's Mount is a small granite cupola surrounded on the landward side by a 'cape' of metamorphosed mudstones. The granite on the seaward side is cut by numerous parallel, steeply inclined mineralized veins, known as a sheeted vein complex. This part of the island is on private land, and not only is permission required to visit it, but it is a

Rhyolite dyke at Sydney Cove, west side of Praa Sands

Site of Special Geological Interest. The wall-rock alteration around the veins is known as greisen. Here, volatiles from the granite have altered the feldspar to produce a quartz- and mica-rich rock with topaz. The quartz veins contain both coarse cassiterite (tin ore) and wolframite (tungsten ore). These greisen veins extend out into the country rocks, with pale sericite mica on the edges of the veins. Elsewhere, a later sulphide vein contains a rare sulphide of tin known as stannite; both topaz and beryl have also been recorded from the island.

At **Sydney Cove**, Praa Sands, at the western end of the beach is an exposure of a rhyolite known locally as elvan. It is unusual

  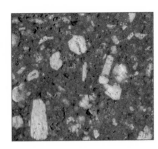

Left to right: Elvan (rhyolite) contact with metasedimentary country rocks; elvan (rhyolite) chilled margin country rock contact; close-up of the rhyolite dyke showing the feldspars and quartz. Granite contact with metasedimenary country rocks on the north-east side of the beach (below)

to see such an example so clearly exposed; those found inland are usually covered over or decomposed. Here the sea keeps the exposure relatively clean, and the rock is comparatively fresh. This rhyolite has been intruded as a vertical sheet called a dyke into the country rocks of dark, metamorphosed mudstones. It was intruded as a magma, and may have fed volcanoes at the surface; it is related to the later stages of granite intrusion. As it intruded, the margins were cooled rapidly, forming a fine-grained, chilled edge which is clearly exposed here. The rock is composed of feldspar crystals and quartz in fine-grained ground mass of quartz and feldspar. Further along the beach, peat, clay and gravel are exposed. These recent sediments

Praa Sands, clockwise from above left: Peat and clay with gravel under blown sand; large crystals of feldspar in granite close to the contact; periglacial head of broken rock fragments, east side of beach

formed after the end of the last ice age, some 10,000 years ago, as the sea level rose and a storm beach advanced inland, trapping a freshwater lagoon behind. These are now covered by sand dunes, and periodically after storms more of the peat is exposed. Further along, the cliffs are composed of periglacial head of angular metasedimentary rock fragments and brown clay formed at the end of the last ice age. At the far south-eastern end of the beach, the Tregonning-Godolphin granite – the gently inclined contact with metasedimenty country rock – is exposed.

Along the coast at **Rinsey Cove**, below the engine-house of the old copper mine of Wheal Prosper, is an exposure of a roof pendant of metasedimenty rock surrounded by the Tregonning-Godolphin granite. A roof pendant is, as it name implies, a remnant of the country rock hanging down, in this case into the granite. On the beach below, the contact between the two rock types can be seen on the wave-cut platform. In the granite on the western side of the beach are xenoliths, or enclaves of country rock, one of which is quite large and has coarse crystals of granite pegmatite under it. Others, in more

Rinsey Cove: Looking east, showing the roof pendant (top); contact between granite and country rock (above)

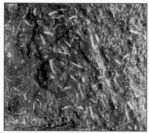

Rinsey Cove, left to right: Xenolith or enclave of country rock with pegmatite below; the metamorphic mineral andalusite in metasedimentary rocks; folded quartz veins in metasementary rocks. Wave-cut platform of slates (below)

ghostly outline, can be seen nearby. On the metasedimentary rock wave-cut platform can be seen the metamorphic minerals andalusite and cordierite. In cliffs behind are quartz veins. These formed in folds when the rock was stressed, and water with silica in solution migrated into lower-pressure areas such as this, crystallizing out prior to the granite intrusion.

Below Tremearne Cliff lies **Megiliggar Rocks**, well known as an exposure of pegmatite and aplite sheets in the country rocks. These are sheets extending out from the main mass of the Tregonning-Godolphin granite on the eastern side. They exploited the horizontal weaknesses in the country rocks when the magma was being intruded.

Clockwise from top left: Pale-coloured granite sheets, Tremearne Cliff to the south-east, looking from Trewarvas Head; Megiliggar Rocks looking towards Trewarvas Head with pegmatite and aplite at the base of Tremearne Cliff; bridging veins of pegmatite and aplite; coarse-grained pegmatite and fine-grained aplite

Porthleven with stormy seas

As they penetrated, bridging veins extending vertically would close off a block of country rock, which would then fall into the granite melt. This process of stoping, or mining, of the country rock would lead to a pressure change, causing the molten granite to freeze and form a fine-grained granitic rock called an aplite, and 'glue' it together. The coarser, crystallized rock, which had time to cool slowly, formed a pegmatite. This would happen many times as the block descended slowly, resulting in layers of aplite and pegmatite so clearly shown in examples on the beach.

On the western side of Porthleven village, south-east of **Parc Trammel Cove**, lying on the wave-cut platform, is a most unusual rock, isolated and different in colour from the surrounding rocks of metamorphosed mudstones. The rock, known as **Giant's Rock**, is probably a glacial erratic of garnet-bearing

Clockwise from above left: Contact between interbedded sandstones and mudstones (grey) with volcanic rock (above) south-east of Porthleven; turbidites of fine sediments, north-east of Porthleven; erratic on wave-cut platform at Parc Trammel Cove, north-west of Porthleven

gneiss. It may have been ice-rafted there by an iceberg which eventually grounded on a high tide. The rock is resistant to erosion, being very hard, and has therefore been isolated up to the present day. On the eastern side of the village of Porthleven lies the contact between basic volcanic rocks extruded into soft mudstones. These fine-grained sedimentary rocks, known as turbidites, formed layers of different-coloured sediment of silts and clays when deposited under the sea. All have been deformed or folded, some intensely, prior to the granite intrusion.

Polurrian Cove

4 The Lizard: Polurrian to Mên-aver Beach

This is a very special area of geological interest, as it comprises rocks rare in the British Isles, and unique in England. The nearest outcrop in Britain is in Scotland, and further away on the Shetland Isles. The rocks of the

Lizard contain a suite from the earth's mantle to the crust, formed in the mid-ocean ridges, which are splitting apart. A simplified section from the top down is as follows:

- sediments of clay and volcanic ash, with silica from fossil debris forming chert deposited on the deep ocean floor
- pillow lavas of basalts extruded on the seafloor
- sheeted dykes of basalt and dolerite, which were the feeder systems for the pillow lavas from an underlying magma chamber
- gabbro intrusions in layers, which were the reservoirs for the basalts above
- ultramafic rocks, which form the earth's mantle of peridotites.

The boundary between the crust and the mantle occurs between the gabbro and the peridotite. This boundary, due to a variation in seismic velocity because of an increase in the density in the rocks, is known as the 'Moho' (or Mohorovicic Discontinuity). These rocks were thrust up northwards (obducted), due to plate movements starting from the Late Devonian Period, to their present position, and bounded by the Lizard Boundary Fault. Hydrothermal waters altered the peridotite

Lizard Boundary Fault with fault breccia in the foreground, Polurrian Cove

into the wonderfully coloured serpentine (serpentinite). This suite of rocks, corresponding to a slice of an ancient ocean floor, is known as an ophiolite, and is one of the best examples in Britain. The topography of the Lizard area is one of a flat plateau to the cliff edge, representing an old erosion surface cut into only by river valleys, and is mainly due to the soft rocks of the peninsula.

At **Polurrian Cove**, the Lizard Boundary Fault is clearly exposed in the cliff, and at low tide, the breccia of broken rocks infilling the fault is exposed. On the north side are Devonian metasedimentary rocks of slates, and on the south side are hornblende schists. This

Polurrian Cove, left to right: Mudstones on the north side of the fault; Lizard Boundary Fault breccia; hornblende schist on the south side of the fault. Mullion Cove looking out to Mullion Island (below)

Copper mining took place a little way inland during the 1800s, when native copper was discovered in large sheets in the rock. Off-shore from the harbour lies Mullion Island which is not accessible; here there are exposures of pillow lavas, cherts and limestones. Further south, at **Kynance Cove**, two types of serpentinite rocks are exposed – bastite and tremolite – which represent hydrothermally altered mantle peridotites.

Below Lizard Village, near Lizard Point, lies **Polpeor Cove** where the geology varies from hornblende schist to mica schist and eventually, in rocks offshore, to gneiss. The best view of these exposures is from above the old lifeboat station at Polpeor Cove. The Man o' War Gneiss, lying offshore as small islands, is the oldest rock in South West

fault zone divides the ophiolite rocks from the rest of Cornwall, running across the Lizard from here on the south-west side to Porthallow (page 74) on the north-eastern side of the peninsula.

At **Mullion Cove** is the boundary between the serpentinite rock and hornblende schist.

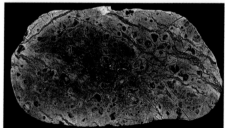

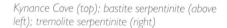

Kynance Cove (top); bastite serpentinite (above left); tremolite serpentinite (right)

England, and represents a metamorphosed granite from margins of the old super-continent of Gondwanda some 500 Ma old. The mica schists are associated with basalts in Polpeor Cove, having been metamorphosed at higher temperatures and pressures than

Lizard Point: Polpeor Cove geology (top); folded Man o' War Gneiss (above left); folded schist (above right)

Kennack Sands beach

other rocks in Cornwall, and are probably a similar age to the Man o' War Gneiss.

Kennack Sands is divided into two small beaches. On both sides there are wonderful exposures of serpentinite – peridotite altered to highly coloured red and green serpentine minerals. On the western side are exposed more unaltered ultrabasic rocks, dark green to black peridotite and a reddish and black-coloured gneiss. The gneiss here is known as the Kennack Gneiss, which has a banded appearance comprising a mixture of granite

Kennack Sands, clockwise from top left: peridotite boulders; peridotite; peridotite altered to colourful serpentinite; asbestoform mineral; Kennack gneiss; green saponite or soapstone veins

and basaltic rocks that were injected along at the base and occasionally into the peridotite. This gneiss probably formed by the melting at depth of the hornblende schist into these two components. On this side of the beach can be seen an asbestos mineral occurring in 'veins' in the cliff, as well as green soapstone (saponite).

Coverack harbour and beach showing the Moho (top). Left to right above: serpentinised peridotite, troctolite and gabbro, all at Coverack

Coverack is a very special place geologically, in that at low tide you can walk over the 'Moho' – the boundary between the mantle and the crust. Starting from the harbour, the rocks are peridotite, representing the upper mantle, mostly altered to serpentinite. As you

loess

Clockwise from top left: Crousa Gravels west of St Keverne; crusairs, just west of St Keverne; brown loess with raised beach at Lowland Point; Lowland Point; close-up of Crousa Gravels

Godrevy Cove, the Lizard, left to right: Basalt dyke cutting through gabbro; detail of basalt with white feldspar crystals

progress across the boundary there is a rare, highly coloured red and white transition rock of troctolite with the black and white gabbro. The gabbroic rocks cut by basaltic dykes, on the far side of the beach away from the harbour, represent the oceanic crust. Above Coverack inland are the Crousa Downs Gravels, a relatively recent, possibly 2 Ma, deposit of material which probably derived from the north. It comprises mainly resistant quartz gravels in a clay matrix. About a kilometre away to the east, also inland, are large gabbro boulders lying on the surface. These are known locally as crusairs, and are core stones, left after the rest of the rock was totally decomposed. These are the gabbro equivalents of tors in the granite.

To the north-east of Coverack lies **Lowland Point**. Here, in flat promontory, just a few metres above high water, are unusual sediments which indicate Cornwall's recent cold past. An orange-brown, silty-clay binds rounded rock cobbles. The silty-clay is the result of wind-blown material accumulating during an ice age when conditions were so cold there was little vegetation. This material is known as loess. Here in the lower part it binds a raised beach.

In this black sandy cove below St Keverne, at **Godrevy Cove**, are excellent exposures of black basaltic dykes cutting through gabbro. These represent the sheeted dykes feeding the pillow lavas which were being extruded on to the ocean floor.

Porthallow beach looking north to Nare Head (above). Quartzite outcrop, north of Porthallow, Nare head in the background (left). Detail of Ordovician quartzite, between Porthallow and Nare Head (below left)

Near the Coast Path to Nare Point, just to the north of **Porthallow**, lies a curious white rock outcrop of quartzite. This is Ordovician Age sandstone, and is older than the slates that enclose it. It is a fragment dislodged from the edge of continental landmass of the old continent Gondwana, which fell into ocean sediments that became Devonian rocks of slates and shales.

Past Nare Point, at **Mên-aver Beach**, is an exposure of a conglomerate of pebbles of

Clockwise from top left: Mên-aver beach looking west towards Gillan Creek; conglomerate outcrop looking north towards Mawnan; striped rock of mudstones and sandstones, Mên-aver beach; conglomerate, Mên-aver beach

many different rock types in sandstone, and elsewhere striped slates and sandstones of Devonian age. The conglomerates and sandstones represent the infill of deep marine channels on an ancient seafloor. The beach here is at the mouth of the **Helford Estuary**, a drowned valley or ria formed at the end of the last ice age.

Carn Brea from Basset Mine (above). Facing page: South Crofty Mine, Pool, Camborne (top); engine houses on the Great Flat Lode (bottom)

5 Carnmenellis: Camborne to Helston

The Camborne-Helston area is mainly underlain by the Carnmenellis Granite, which extends from the outskirts of Camborne in the north to Helston in the south. Outliers are Carn Brea above Camborne-Redruth and Carn Marth to the east. On the flanks of the northern periphery are not only the famous copper and tin orefield of Camborne and Redruth around Carn Brea, but also small, scattered areas of tin mineralization that occur throughout the granite and nearby metamorphic aureole. It is at Camborne that the last working tin mine in Cornwall ceased production at the end of the last century.

Porkellis Moor, showing alluvial mine workings of pits and hummocks

Each side of **Carn Brea** – the hill with a monument towering above the Camborne area – has been extensively mined. The majority of the economic mineralization followed the contact between the country rocks of Devonian slates and volcanic rocks. It is here that **South Crofty**, the last producing tin mine in Cornwall, ceased operations in 1998. However, exploration continues today (2011) underground to prove up an economic deposit.

To the south of Carn Brea, and in a 'saddle ' of country rocks between it and Four Lanes, lay the **Great Flat Lode**. Mines on this structure, which extended for almost 5 km, exploited it primarily for tin ore. It is a large-scale mineralized fault which has been mined to a depth exceeding 600 m. The old pump-engine houses stretch out into the distance following the line of the lode.

Further into the granite, near **Porkellis**, is a low-lying wetland which was once worked for alluvial cassiterite (tin oxide), brought down by rivers at the end of the last ice age by catastrophic floods due to summer melts of snow. Cassiterite had concentrated out at the bottom of the sediments on the bedrock as it is denser than quartz and feldspar. It was probably quite rich here, as tin-bearing lodes outcrop in the valley bottom and sides. This tin ore was easy to mine, because only the overburden needed to be removed and the gravel washed with water to remove the waste, leaving the heavy mineral of cassiterite. The hummocky, wet landscape it left is now an important wetland. Ancient miners have left their trace, not only in the landscape but in mortar stones, used for crushing the ore, near **Poldark Mine** at Wendron. Placer deposits of this type were worked from prehistoric times all over Cornwall in river valleys and low-lying areas. The waste products produced from mining were discharged into the streams, and have silted up many an estuary in the county.

Part of Porkellis Moor with Basset and Grylls Mine on the left (top). Alluvial cassiterite (above left). Mortar stone for crushing alluvial tin ore, Poldark Mine, Wendron (above right)

Godrevy beach looking towards Godrevy Point

6 North Coast: Godrevy to Perranporth

Starting from Godrevy Beach and ending at Ligger Point, just north of Perranporth, the geology ranges from soft sediments of very recent age in geological terms (Quaternary Age) to tin mineralization related to the granite intrusion (Permian Age), and to an earlier mineralizing episode containing iron of Middle Devonian Age.

At **Godrevy Point**, the Devonian Age sediments of turbidites are folded by past tectonic events. However, the exposure

Godrevy, clockwise from top left: Raised beach cemented with manganese and iron oxides; folded sedimentary rocks; sand rock of cemented sand with beach cobbles

in the cliffs along the beach shows a clear example of climate change in the recent geological past. Starting from near Godrevy Point there are exposures of sandrock. This was formed at a period of higher sea level during an interglacial some 190,000 years ago when the climate was warmer. Once these were sand dunes, which became cemented by the calcium carbonate from the shells they contain and have now turned into a rock – a process called lithification. Other examples of raised beach abound around this site, some cemented by iron oxides and black manganese from waters seeping out at the base. All

Raised beach overlain by blown sand and head with erratic in the foreground, Godrevy (left). Looking towards St Agnes Head, with Wheal Coates Engine Houses (right)

lie on Devonian Age slates with quartz veins; some near the point show examples of folding. Further back along the beach, the raised beach is overlain with head – a periglacial product produced during an ice age, when the ground was frozen and Cornwall had tundra-like climate. Accumulations of loess – a wind-blown silty-clay – and rock debris, in this case quartz fragments, migrated downslope to fill in valleys and small embayments like coves. This in turn has been covered by dune deposits of sand which accumulated after the end of the last ice age, some 10,000 years ago. At one site, **Godrevy Rocks**, is a glacial erratic at the base of the cliff – probably a product of a beached iceberg.

The area near St Agnes village is dominated by **St Agnes Beacon**, a small, isolated topographic high, which may have been a small island at some stage during the Miocene or Pliocene, 20–2 Ma. At the base of the hill on the seaward side lies a crescent-shaped deposit of sands and clays. These have been exploited for the clay content, and the sands for moulding purposes in local iron foundries in the past. Examination of these deposits suggests a wind-blown origin. Around the beacon, which lies close to a granite outcrop, the area has been extensively mineralized with rich tin-bearing ores, and is a famous mining district. At **Wheal Coates**, a celebrated landmark, the geological structure is clearly

Clockwise from top left: Wheal Coates lode exposure showing the rhyolite capping the lode, St Agnes; Trevaunance Cove with mine tips above; fault at Trevaunance Cove

visible at low tide in the cliff below the engine houses. Here a rhyolite or elvan dyke caps the underlying tin lode. To the north-east, at **Trevaunance Cove** in the high cliffs near the beach, with the mine dumps above, is an example of how the tin lodes, which run almost parallel to the cliff and dip seaward, were disrupted by other faults.

Just south-west of Perranporth is the granite outcrop of **Cligga Head**, a famous geological site. The headland and adjacent cliffs are honeycombed with old mine tunnels.

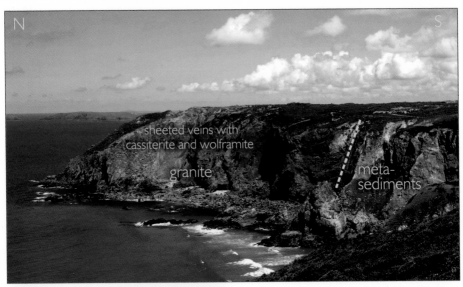

sheeted veins with
cassiterite and wolframite

granite

meta-
sediments

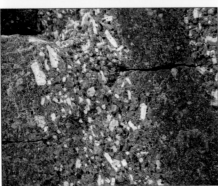

*Cligga Head: Granite outcrop and contact with
metasedimentary rocks (top); detail of greisen
veins with granite between (left)*

The granite here has been cut by a sheeted
vein complex, similar to that exposed at
St Michael's Mount (page 54) in the west.
These veins have greisen borders where the
feldspars have been replaced with quartz,
mica and topaz by mineralizing fluids that had
been trapped towards the top of the granite.
These fractures have been further mineral-

Cligga Head: Iron-stained cliffs near the headland (left); cassiterite in quartz (above); sheeted greisen vein outcrop (lower left)

ized with wolfram (tungsten ore) and cassiterite (tin ore), and were last mined during the Second World War. In the quarry there is an excellent exposure of sheeted veins with greisen borders.

At **Perranporth**, to the north-east, is an extensive dune field of wind-blown sand; most has accumulated as a result of a rising sea level after the last ice age some 10,000 years ago, as the storm beach advanced landwards. At the northern end of the beach is an iron lode outcrop of the **Perran Iron Mine**, last worked in the Second World War. This enigmatic deposit infills a great fault which runs for many kilometres inland. Here haematite and other iron ores were extracted. It is assumed that this deposit formed in the Middle

Perranporth beach looking north-east towards Ligger Point (top). Sea-eroded faults near Ligger Point, north of Perranporth (left). Perran Iron Lode and old mine workings (above)

Devonian Age by ascending mineral-bearing waters in a great fault. Further north, at **Ligger Point**, are excellent examples of the sea exploiting weaknesses in the cliff where there are major faults cutting through the rocks.

Watergate Bay, Newquay

7 North Coast: Newquay to Trebetherick

Here are mainly soft rocks of Devonian marine sediments which have been mildly metamorphosed, producing shales and slates during folding, but which are generally outside the influence of the granite intrusion. It is in this area that rare limestones are exposed in a cliff. Occasionally, Devonian volcanism produced both extrusive pillow lavas on the seabed and into the soft marine sediments, and also intrusive dolerite bodies which were the feeders for the extrusive rocks of basalt

Clockwise from top left: Part of a fish fossil in black on grey shales, Watergate Bay, Newquay; Trevose Head; highly coloured volcanic rock, Trevose Head; impression of Devonian Pteraspid fish

above. It is from the area here and extending northwards that, rarely, fossils are found, including the remains of an early fish.

At **Watergate Bay**, north of Newquay, in the cliffs on the more northerly side of the bay, are fish beds in Devonian purple and green, folded sediments. Here, although known as fish beds, only occasionally can small fragments of the Devonian Age armoured fish known as a Pteraspid be found,

as black remains in the pale slates and shales. The cliffs here are up to 80 m high, but due to their soft nature are prone to large falls on to the beach below.

Up the coast, at **Trevose Head**, Devonian volcanic activity is in evidence where basalts have intruded into soft marine sediments below the lighthouse. Above, in the quarry, is an exposure of highly coloured rocks of probable volcanic origin.

Clockwise from top left: Outcropping slates, Harlyn Bay; Trevone Bay; cleavage in slates near Trevone; dolerite outcrop, St Cadoc's Point, Trevone

Further along the coast, at **Harlyn Bay**, outcropping slates are exposed on the beach with occasional sandrock above, very similar to that found at Godrevy near Hayle (pages 80–82). The beach is backed by recent sand dunes. At **Trevone Beach**, near Roundhole Point, are volcanic rocks of dolerite, and nearby is a large feature known as **Round Hole** which, as its name implies, is a large opening – a spectacular and unusual collapsed sea cave, where the sea has exploited weaknesses along two faults. Eventually, as it made progress inland, the roof caved in to produce the apparent excavation in the field. Just around the Point is an area named **Marble Cliff**. Here, beds of white limestone

Purple and green slates, near Stepper Point

alternate with dark beds of mudstones exposed in a cliff some 80 m high. Although they are almost horizontal, they are upside down due to folding, with the youngest beds at the bottom of the cliff. Near to **Stepper Point**, further east, folded purple and pale green slates in the high cliff are exposed to erosion by the sea.

Clockwise from top left: Marble Cliff Beds of alternating limestone and shale, Trevone Bay; purple and green slates, Trebetherick, looking towards Stepper Point; Daymer Bay, looking towards Padstow on the other side of the Camel Estuary

On the opposite side of the Camel Estuary from Padstow, at **Trebetherick**, around Daymer Bay, are wonderful exposures of purple and green Devonian Age slates in stripes. Some of the most spectacular examples are to be seen near **Trebetherick Point**, on the northern side of the bay. The colours probably derive from trace chemicals they contain from volcanic eruptions as the sediments were deposited under the sea.

Delabole Slate Quarry

8 North Coast: Delabole to Bude

In this area there is a change in age of the sedimentary rocks from Devonian in the southern part near Delabole up to Tintagel, and then Carboniferous from here to beyond Bude to the north, continuing to the border

Delabole Slate Quarry: Prepared Delabole slate (left); Spirifer fossil – 'Delabole Butterfly' (right)

with Devon. The sediments laid down in the Devonian seabed in this part of Cornwall are quite fine-grained mudstones, but the Carboniferous rocks further north are of sandstones and mudstones which alternate to give beds of different hardness, which are termed turbidites. These were formed in the deep sea, when the coarser sediments, such as sands, settled out first, with finer clay sediments above. This movement may well have been triggered by earthquakes disturbing the soft sediments and causing them to move further down the continental slope, or it may have been due to the action of gravity. Much later, when the sediments were turning into rocks, the area was subjected to severe pressure as plates moved into each other, resulting in intense folding. Some of the best

examples of folding in Cornwall are exposed in sections along this coast.

Next to the village of Delabole, near Camelford, lies **Delabole Slate Quarry**, England's oldest slate quarry, having been worked for over 600 years. Now a huge open pit over 130 m deep, it can be viewed from a platform kindly provided by the owners. The slate here is composed of very fine-grained sediments – a mudstone laid on the seabed. This has been the focus of what is termed regional metamorphism, after being subjected to stress, which caused an alignment of the minerals to produce a perfect cleavage, hence the rock can be split easily to be used as roofing tiles. Other, smaller quarries in the area produce thicker slabs of coloured slate for decorative purposes; the colour is

Trebarwith Strand beach looking out to Gull Rock (left). Volcanic bombs overlying rocks of fine-grained marine sediments, Trebarwith Strand (right)

caused by iron-oxide staining as they lie near the surface. It is in the Delabole quarry that the famous Delabole 'butterflies' have been found. These are, in fact, the distorted fossil shells of *Spirifer vermuli*, a fossil brachiopod.

On the coast, down a steeply wooded valley with abandoned slate quarries, to the north-west of Delabole, lies **Trebarwith Strand** near to Tintagel Head. Near the car-park, before the village on the northern side, notice a pale grey rock, above which is an overhanging stratum of what looks like more angular debris. The lower, fine-grained rock was laid down in quiet water, whereas the one above represents a period of intense explosive volcanic undersea activity, which produced volcanic bombs of lava and ash. Both rocks are Lower Carboniferous in age. On approaching the beach near the car-park, these volcanic bombs have been compressed and stressed and now look like thick, stacked pancakes. Underfoot nearby you can see sporadic pink calcite. On the beach, exposed as the tide goes out, are examples of the volcanic bombs as seen from above – eroded by the sea to fully expose their geometry.

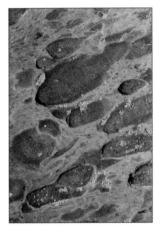

Left to right (above): Trebarwith Strand, stacked 'pancakes' of volcanic bombs; plan view of volcanic bombs; pink calcite. Tilted Carboniferous strata, Crackington Haven (below)

The rocks at Crackington Haven and Millook Haven, near Bude, are Carboniferous in age and are known as the **Culm Measures**. Variation in the strata's hardness, because they are alternate beds of sandstone and siltstone which have been folded and tilted, produces very interesting beach profiles and cliffscapes. At **Crackington Haven**, the tilted strata are clearly exposed on the beach, and in some cases these have been cut by quartz veins carrying the iron carbonate mineral siderite. Occasionally trace fossils

Millook Haven: the beach (above); spectacular chevron folding in Carboniferous sediments (right)

can be seen in the rocks as paler-coloured sediments. These soft-bodied organisms, such as worms, have left a trace of where they burrowed into the sediment under the sea, but no trace remains of the animal itself.

At **Millook Haven**, just to the north, is the very impressive high cliff of strata deformed into 'chevron' folds by the collision of continental plates in the geological past.

Bude is famous for folds and other geological structures exposed in the cliffs and foreshore. On the northern side of **Compass Point** are the classic folded rock formations exposed on the beach. Here you can see the folds not only in section from the 'front', but also from above and, where an area has been eroded, in 'plan' view. These features have been much visited and photographed! Looking closely at the rock outcrop, you can see evidence of the movement of water on the old seabed in the form of ripple marks now preserved in the rock.

Facing page, Crackington Haven, clockwise from top left: Carboniferous strata outcrop on the beach; quartz veins with siderite; trace fossil outline; quartz veining in Carboniferous sediments

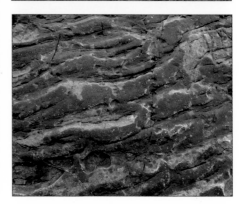

Compass Point, Bude beach, clockwise from top left: Bude beach from the entrance to the canal; 'Whale Rock' front section; ripple marks; 'Whale Rock' from above

Restronguet Creek, Devoran, Carnon Downs

9 Falmouth: Carnon Downs to Nare Head

The area from Falmouth to Nare Head, near Veryan, includes recent geology (Quaternary) of a drowned river valley, and tin deposits formed during lower sea levels, as well as beach deposits when sea levels were

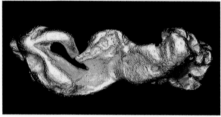

Clockwise from top left: Carnon River, Carnon Valley viaduct in the background; ruins of Carnon Mine; gold nugget from the Carnon Valley

much higher than today. The drowned valleys – rias – were formed during an interglacial – the period between ice ages – when the sea level rose relative to the land.

The **Carrick Roads** is part of the Fal Estuary, which extends for many kilometres inland. This is part of a deep ria which probably also extends for many kilometres offshore. The valley was eroded at times of very low sea levels during ice ages in the glacial period, when sea levels were up to 120 m lower than today. Radiating off this estuary is **Restronguet Creek**, part of the Carnon River, and also a drowned valley. As the climate warmed up and formed an interglacial, and before the sea level encroached, torrential flood waters from summer melts of snow brought down tremendous amounts of gravely sediment from the hinterland.

The **Carnon River** drained an important orefield to the north-west in the Gwennap District, known for its copper and tin mines in the eighteenth and nineteenth centuries. River sediments carried quantities of cassiterite (tin oxide), which is over 2.5 times more dense than quartz. The cassiterite sank to the valley floor and was concentrated there as

Pendower and Carne Beach: Looking towards Nare Head (above); raised beach overlying the bedrock on a wave-cut platform (right)

alluvial, or placer, deposit. The rise in sea level deposited thick estuarine muds up to 10 m thick further down the valley. In **Restronguet Creek**, these buried alluvial tin deposits were exploited by sinking a shaft in rock on the edge of the creek, tunnelling out from the bottom to reach the valley bottom, and excavating the tin gravels. All mining operations, especially at high tide, took place under the sea. They were the **Carnon Mine** and Restronguet Mines of the nineteenth century.

At **Pendower and Carne Beach** overlooking Nare Head, near Veryan, is an excellent example of a raised beach in the cliff. The beaches lie on a wave-cut platform of Devonian Age slates and shales, formed when the climate was warmer and the sea level higher during an interglacial between two ice ages. Rounded beach pebbles and sands have been cemented by manganese and iron from waters running through them. Above are deposits of periglacial head from the last ice age which ended some 10,000 years ago, so we know the beach is older than the deposit above. On the shore east of the raised beach is a gully, where the sea has exploited

Pendower and Carne Beach: Fault exploited by sea erosion (top); limestone outcrop (above left); quartzite boulders and interbedded sandstones and mudstones (above right.)

a weakness in the rock caused by a fault. Further east, at **Carne**, the bedrock, some 380 million years old, carries rare Devonian Age limestones, and quartzite boulders. The quartzites are older than the slates, shales and limestones, being from the Ordovician Period. They were once sandstones, and were incorporated into these marine deposits by instability during a mountain-building episode due to tectonic plate movements.

Greensplat china clay pit, St Austell

10 St Austell: Indian Queens to Fowey

Part of the main granite intrusion in the St Austell area is one of the most kaolinized in the world. Extensive quarrying or mining operations continue today, with very large open pits extracting china clay. These can

St Austell area, clockwise from top left: Old china clay tip; kaolinized granite; hydrothermal breccia, Wheal Remfry near Indian Queens

best be seen by air. One exception is at the **Wheal Martyn Museum**, where a viewing platform has been provided to observe a working pit. Other granitic intrusion-related events have produced breccias, quartz and tourmaline rocks known as schorl, quartz and feldspar rocks, and a rock type once quarried for decorative stone.

Kaolinization is the result of weak acidic waters attacking and breaking down the feldspar in granite to a white clay named kaolin, with the quartz and micas left intact. This prob-

ably started not long after the granite was emplaced, with fracturing and minor mineralizing fluids passing through the rock preparing it for downward water to decay the feldspars into kaolinite (china clay) in later geological time. The huge tips of waste, known locally as stent, are of quartz and unkaolinized granite, and mica dams, or slurry pools, can be seen covering large areas of the granite mass, mainly north and east of **St Austell**.

It was during granite emplacement that volatiles and water accumulated under the

St Austell area, left to right above: Tourmalinite or quartz-tourmaline rock, Roche Rock; pegmatite, Tresayes Quarry; luxullianite. Roche Rock, Roche (below)

roof of the granite. When the pressure of this overcame the weight of the rocks above, it exploded upwards to the surface, producing a fragmented rock called a hydrothermal breccia. These occur in some of the clay pits, but the best example lies at the west end of the St Austell granite at **Wheal Remfry**, near the village of Indian Queens.

To the north and west are three interesting rock types, two of which are highly coloured. The first results from an accumulation of boron- and silica-bearing fluids in the upper part of the granite, producing a very resistant quartz and tourmaline rock known as a tourmalinite or schorl rock. This occurs as a dramatic outcrop rising out of the ground at **Roche Rock**, which is topped by an ancient hermitage. Nearby, at **Tresayes**, a coarse-grained granitic rock called a peg-

matite was quarried in the past for the large feldspars used in glass-making. This rock type is the result of slow-cooling fluids from the granite producing a rock of mainly feldspar and quartz. A decorative rock was once exploited at Luxulyan. Here the granite has undergone a process of tourmalinization, due to solutions rich in boron replacing some of the minerals with black tourmaline and turning the feldspars red. An excellent example

Fowey town on the drowned River Fowey – a ria

of polished luxullianite can be seen in the church at **Lanlivery**.

To the east of St Austell, beyond Gribbin Head, lies the drowned river valley, or ria, at **Fowey**.

11 Kingsand

Kingsand, in Cawsand Bay, at the beach running north-east of the village on the foreshore, is a fascinating geological exposure.

Here Permian Age rhyolite lava is exposed as a red rock with crude columnar jointing. The composition of this igneous rock is similar to that of granite, and demonstrates that there was volcanic activity during granitic intrusion. Being rich in silica, and hence viscous, the volcanic activity at the time would have been most explosive! The outcrop of lava has a flat top caused by a period of higher sea level producing a wave-cut platform. Further to the north-east there is a change in the geology. Exposed under the lava, and gently inclined, lies a red rock composed of cemented

Kingsand beach, clockwise from top left: Looking towards rhyolite outcrop; rhyolite outcrop showing crude columnar structure; detail of rhyolite

Kingsand, clockwise from top left: Devonian Age sandstone outcrop; unconformity between Permian conglomerate (left) and Devonian sandstones (right); quartz veins in Devonian sandstone; Permian Age conglomerate outcrop under the rhyolite

pebbles and cobbles of different rock types, known as a conglomerate. This is a Permian Age sedimentary rock produced by sporadic flash-floods transporting and depositing them during a desert climate. Adjacent to this are more steeply dipping red rocks of sandstone of Devonian Age. The junction of these two rocks is known as an unconformity. The conglomerate is about 290 million years old, the sandstone 390 million years old, so there is an age gap of 100 million years missing from the geological records at the junction between these two rock types. This unconformity can be seen more clearly on the beach when the sand has been removed by tidal action.

Brown Willy, Cornwall's highest point, from Buttern Hill, Bodmin Moor

12 Bodmin Moor: Camelford to Minions

The Bodmin granite is the largest mass of all the granite outcrops in Cornwall, forming an extensive area of bleak moorland and dramatic granite tors. The area has three platforms or plateaus from 150 to 200 m,

Rough Tor, Bodmin Moor

230 to 250 m, and a high one of 300 m. These platforms have been interpreted as areas produced by wave action, either when sea levels were higher, or, most probably, due to uplift raising the land out of the sea. As yet there is no fossil evidence to support this. The high platform at 300 m was used during the Second World War as an airfield, at **Davidstow**, where extensive vestiges in the form of runways are still in evidence.

Rising up out of the platforms are distinctive tors, one of which, **Brown Willy**, at 420 m, is Cornwall's highest point. Tor for-

mation is produced by tropical weathering in the Cenozoic Era leaving behind the more resistant rock. This was followed in more recent geological time – the Quaternary in the ice ages – by frost action producing dramatic outcrops of granite. An excellent example of the way the granite jointing is exposed to weathering occurs at **Rough Tor**, where the almost horizontal off-loading and vertical joints are clearly seen. One of the most spectacular tors on Rough Tor is **Showery Tor**, at the northern end. The scree, or boulder-field of rocks on the slopes of the tors, is called

Bodmin Moor, clockwise from above left: Showery Tor with old Stannon china clay pit in the background; clitter blocks of granite on the slopes of Rough Tor; Lanlavery Rock quartz vein outcrop, Davidstow Moor

clitter. These loose rocks were broken off by frost action, and moved by the action of gravity during summer melt when the permafrost thawed, in a process known as solifluction.

Mineralization is sporadic on and around the moor, except the south-eastern area around **Minions**. Here rich deposits of both tin and copper have been exploited in the past, leaving behind only spoil tips and derelict engine houses. Elsewhere on the moor, very small isolated placer deposits of tungsten and tin were mined in the early twentieth century, as at **Buttern Hill** near **Altarnun** during the Second World War, and at **Trewint**. Near Davidstow, on the southern part of **Davidstow Moor**, lies an extensive outcrop of a white quartz vein many metres wide, in places 3–4 m high, and up to 1 km long. The best exposure is at **Lanlavery Rock**. At the north-eastern end, copper was mined at **Roughtor Mine**. Nineteenth-century reports suggest that the quartz vein carried trace amounts of gold! Evidence of near-

Gravel quarrying at Trewint, Altarnun (above). Cheesewring Quarry in granite, Bodmin Moor (left). Granite cobbles from Trewint Alluvials (below left); wolframite (black) in quartz, Stannon River near Rough Tor (below right)

surface deep weathering, preceded by earlier hydrothermal activity, is indicated by small areas where china clay has been exploited in the past over the moor. One such activity was at **Stannon**, near Rough Tor, which only ceased operation in 2002 and is now a reservoir. Granite quarries have extracted dimension stone in the past – a fine example is the defunct **Cheesewring Quarry** near Minions, while the **De Lank Quarry**, on the northwestern side of the moor, is still active today.

Glossary

acid: **igneous rocks** (e.g., **granite** and **rhyolite**) usually contain abundant light-coloured minerals, such as quartz and feldspar (felsic).

alluvial: relating to the movement by a river and/or deposition in a river or floodplain. Alluvial sediments may be clays, silts, sands or cobble, including boulders.

andalusite: A metamorphic mineral which forms under low pressure and moderate to high temperatures.

anticline: a fold that is convex upwards and has its oldest beds at its core.

antiform: a purely descriptive term for any fold that is convex up. If age relationships between various strata are unknown, the term antiform must be used.

AOD: above Ordnance Datum

aplite: a light-coloured, intrusive **igneous rock** in which quartz and feldspar are the dominant minerals, with the same composition as **granite**. Aplites are usually very fine-grained.

archipelago: a chain or cluster of islands.

basalt: a **mafic** volcanic rock, usually black and fine-grained due to rapid cooling of **lava**, rich in iron and magnesium.

basic: igneous rocks with a lower silica content, and more iron and magnesium dark coloured minerals (**mafic**).

batholith: a large igneous **intrusion** that forms from cooled **magma** in the earth's crust.

breccia: a rock composed of broken fragments of minerals or rock cemented together by a fine-grained matrix which may be similar to or different from the composition of the fragments.

Carboniferous: a period in geological history that extended from the end of the **Devonian** Period (360 **Ma**) to the beginning of the **Permian** Period (299 **Ma**).

Cenozoic: the period from 65.5 million years ago to the present.

chert: a **sedimentary rock** of fine-grained, silica-rich microcrystalline quartz. The silica usually derives from **fossil** organisms.

china clay: a deposit of a white mineral, kaolinite, which is clay formed from the decomposition of feldspars in altered **granite**.

cleavage: the tendency of a rock to break

along preferred planes of weakness that have formed by the alignment of new minerals during regional metamorphism.

conglomerate: a **sedimentary rock** consisting of rounded rock fragments such as pebbles, cobbles and boulders that have become cemented together within a finer-grained matrix.

contact metamorphism: occurs typically around intrusive **igneous rock**s as a result of the temperature increase caused by the intrusion of **magma** into cooler **country rock**, making the country rocks hard and fine-grained.

cordierite: a very hard, dark-coloured mineral produced by the metamorphism of mudstones.

country rock: the rock intruded by and surrounding an igneous **intrusion**.

crust: earth's crust is composed of a great variety of igneous, metamorphic, and sedimentary rocks. It is underlain by the **mantle**.

Devonian: a geologic period and system spanning from 416 to 359 million years ago.

dimension stone: natural rock selected and fabricated to specific shapes or sizes, and usually to required colours, textures, patterns and surface finishes.

dolerite: a medium-grained, basic **igneous rock** of similar composition to **basalt**, usually occurring in **dyke**s or **sill**s. Also called diabase.

dyke: a sheet-like body of **igneous rock** that cuts across layering or contacts in the rock into which it intrudes.

fault: a planar fracture in rock, across which there has been significant sliding displacement (movement).

felsic: a pale-coloured **igneous rock** with abundant light-coloured minerals, such as quartz and feldspar, e.g. **granite**.

fossil: the recognizable remains, such as bones, shells or leaves, or other evidence, such as tracks, burrows, or impressions, of past life on earth.

gabbro: a group of dark, coarse-grained, intrusive **mafic igneous rock**s, chemically equivalent to **basalt**.

glacial period: an interval of time within an ice age that is marked by colder temperatures and glacier advances, with an Arctic-type climate and tundra conditions beyond the ice sheet.

gneiss: higher-temperature **metamorphic rock**s, usually banded in appearance.

granite: a course-grained, **felsic**, **igneous rock** comprising quartz, feldspar and micas.

greenstone: the name comes from the green hue imparted by the colour of the metamorphic minerals within **mafic volcanic** rocks.

greisen: a hard, grey-coloured form of wall-rock alteration caused by **hydrothermal fluid**s altering rocks to a mass of quartz, mica and topaz.

head: an earthy, often chaotic mass of sediments containing angular fragments produced as a result of the slow, downslope movement of material by repeated freezing and thawing processes in **periglacial** regions.

Holocene: the most recent division of geological time, dating back to 10,000 years from the present.

hornfels: a series of dark-coloured, often banded, contact **metamorphic rock**s that have been baked and recrystallized by the heat of igneous **intrusion**, and have been rendered massive, hard, and splintery.

hydrothermal fluids: hot, water-bearing fluids containing minerals which precipitate out into fractures forming **vein**s or **lode**s, and/or chemicals which react with the host rocks that the fluids are passing through to form wall-rock alteration.

ice age: a period of time during which ice sheets and glaciers cover regions that are normally ice-free.

igneous rock: rock is formed by **magma** cooling and becoming solid. Igneous rock may form with or without crystallization, either below the surface as intrusive (plutonic) rocks, or on the surface as extrusive (**volcanic**) rocks.

intrusion: liquid rock that forms under the surface of the earth. **Magma** from under the surface slowly moves its way up from deep within the earth and into any cracks or spaces it can find, sometimes pushing existing **country rock** out of the way.

joint: fracture with no sliding (displacement).

lamprophyre: a type of intrusive **igneous rock** dominated by **mafic** minerals such as biotite mica.

landform: any natural formation, largely defined by its surface form and location in the landscape, and typically an element of topography.

lava: molten rock expelled by a volcano during an eruption.

limestone: a sedimentary rock of calcium carbonate.

lode: a deposit of **metalliferous** ore that fills or is embedded in a fissure (or crack) in a rock formation; also known as a **vein**.

loess: a sediment formed by the accumulation of wind-blown silt and lesser and variable amounts of sand and clay.

Ma: million years ago.

mafic rock: a dark-coloured rock, rich in iron and magnesium, and minerals such as olivine, e.g. **basalt**.

magma: molten rock beneath the surface of the earth.

mantle: rocks below the earth's crust, usually 5–75 km down.

Mesozoic: a group of several periods of geologic time (Triassic, Jurassic, Cretaceous), whose ages range from 248 to 65 **Ma**.

metabasites: basaltic **volcanic** rocks that show evidence of having been subjected to metamorphism.

metalliferous: metal-bearing.

metamorphic aureole: the area surrounding the intrusion where the **contact metamorphism** effects are present. Caused by heat; can extend up to several kilometres.

metamorphic rock: a rock that has undergone mineralogical or textural changes produced by increase in heat or pressure.

metasedimentary rock (metasediments): a **sedimentary rock** that shows evidence of having been subjected to metamorphism.

mineralization: the hydrothermal deposition of economically important metals in the formation of ore bodies or **lode**s.

Moho: also called the Mohorovičić discontinuity – the boundary between the earth's crust and the **mantle**. The Moho separates both oceanic crust and continental crust from underlying mantle.

mudstone: a very fine-grained **sedimentary rock** whose original constituents were clays or silts.

ophiolite: a section of the earth's oceanic crust (typically oceanic sediments, **basalt pillow lava**s, **dolerite**s and **gabbro**s) and the underlying upper **mantle peridotite** that has been thrust adjacent to continental crust.

orogeny: an episode of mountain-building and/or intense rock deformation due to the movement of plates.

pegmatite: a very coarse-grained **igneous rock**. In Cornwall, of mainly granitic composition; usually forms from molten rock rich in water or other volatiles that facilitate the growth of large crystals.

peridotite: a dense, coarse-grained **igneous ultramafic rock**, rich in magnesium. It is the dominant rock of the upper part of the earth's **mantle**.

periglacial: place where processes related to freezing of water occur in an area not buried by glacial ice, but subject to intense freezing cycles; exhibits permafrost weathering and erosion characteristics.

Permian: the period following the **Carboniferous**, extending from 299 to 251 million years ago. It ended with the largest known mass extinction of species.

pillow lava: lavas that contain characteristic pillow-shaped structures, often developed during the extrusion of the lava under water.

placer deposit: alluvial material containing economic amounts of ore minerals; in Cornwall, cassiterite (tin ore) and wolframite (tungsten ore).

plate tectonics: a scientific theory which describes the large-scale motions of earth's crust of ten fragments, or plates, which move in relation to one another, shifting continents, forming new ocean crust, and stimulating **volcanic** eruptions and mountain-building.

Pleistocene: the period of time lasting from about 2 million to 10,000 years ago, and denoted by the alternation between glacial and interglacial stages.

Quaternary: the latest period in geological history, beginning about 2 million years ago; this is divided into two smaller periods of time: the **Pleistocene** and the **Holocene**.

raised beach: beach sediments lying above the high-water mark on a **wave-cut platform** formed during periods of higher sea level.

regional metamorphism: metamorphism affecting a large region that is associated with mountain-building events.

rhyolite: a **felsic** rock which has a similar composition to **granite**.

sandstone: a **sedimentary rock** composed mainly of sand-sized minerals or rock grains.

schist: metamorphic rock, usually derived from fine-grained **sedimentary rock**s, that contains more than 50 per cent platy (thin sheet of mineral) such as mica.

sedimentary basin: any geographical feature exhibiting subsidence and consequent infilling by sedimentation. As the sediments are buried, they are subjected to increasing pressure and begin the process of lithification (turning into rock).

sedimentary rock: a type of rock formed by sedimentation of material at the earth's surface and deposited in layers as strata.

shale: **sedimentary rock** derived from mud, characterized by breaks along thin laminae, or parallel layering, or bedding less than 1 cm in thickness.

sill: a tabular body of intrusive **igneous rock**, parallel to the layering of the rocks into which it intrudes but does not cross-cut.

skarn: calc-silicate rocks intimately associated with **granite intrusion**s.

slate: a fine-grained, homogeneous **metamorphic rock** derived from an original **shale**-type sedimentary rock composed of clay through low-grade regional metamorphism.

slickenside: a smoothly polished surface caused by friction as two sides of rock move against each other on a fault.

stock: a small, igneous **intrusion** often connected to a **batholith**.

stoping: a process during the ascent of **magma** involving the fracturing of the **country rock**. Once fractures are formed, melt and/or volatiles will typically invade, widening the fracture and promoting the release of host rock blocks (stoped blocks) into the melt.

tectonics: the forces and movements that have operated in a region to create geological structures.

tombolo: a deposition landform in which an island is attached to the mainland by a narrow piece of land, e.g. a spit or bar.

Triassic: a geologic period that extended from about 250 to 200 million years ago.

tuff: a rock consisting of consolidated **volcanic** ash ejected from vents during a volcanic eruption.

turbidite: geological formations derive from turbidity current deposits – deposits of variable grain-size from a form of underwater avalanche, often triggered by an earthquake, which is responsible for distributing vast amounts of sediment into the deep ocean.

ultrabasic/ultramafic: an **igneous rock** consisting almost entirely of iron and magnesium, dark-coloured minerals and no free quartz.

unconformity: a break in a sedimentary sequence, or a period of no deposition that represents a gap in geological time.

vein: a distinct, sheet-like body of crystallized minerals in a fault or crack within a rock.

volcanic: rocks formed from the activity of a volcano.

wave-cut platform: a platform formed by wave action that is raised above present sea-level.

Index and Location of Sites